# Slide, Charlie Brown! Slide!

# SLIDE, CHARLIE BROWN! SLIDE!

## CHARLES M. SCHULZ

VOL. II from
IT'S A DOG'S LIFE,
CHARLIE BROWN!

A FAWCETT CREST BOOK

Fawcett Books, Greenwich, Connecticut

*SLIDE, CHARLIE BROWN! SLIDE!*

This book, prepared especially for Fawcett Books,
CBS Publications, CBS Consumer Publishing,
a Division of CBS Inc., comprises the second half of
IT'S A DOG'S LIFE CHARLIE BROWN, and is reprinted
by arrangement with Holt, Rinehart and Winston, Inc.

Printed in the United States of America

36   35   34   33   32   31   30   29   28   27

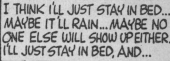

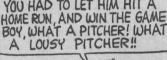

THAT WAS VERY BEAUTIFUL, SCHROEDER...WHAT WAS IT?

THAT WAS BEETHOVEN'S SONATA NO. 11, OPUS 22

NOW YOU HAVE ME WORRIED...

LITTLE BY LITTLE BEETHOVEN IS SNEAKING AROUND, OVER, AND UNDER MY MENTAL BLOCK!

BIRDS THINK I'M INTERESTING!

AND NOW, AFTER LISTENING TO THE NINTH SYMPHONY, WE'RE READY TO SERVE THE CAKE

WOW!

HAPPY BIRTHDAY, BEETHOVEN!

THIS IS A SIMPLE CEREMONY, BUT VERY MEANINGFUL...

I'LL SAY IT IS...YOU'RE GOING TO HAVE TO CUT THE CAKE...MY EYES ARE TOO FULL OF TEARS!

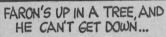